AQA

GCSE french

Exam Skills Workbook

Danièle Bourdais
Sue Finnie

OXFORD
UNIVERSITY PRESS

UNIVERSITY PRESS

Great Clarendon Street, Oxford OX2 6DP

Oxford University Press is a department of the University of Oxford. It furthers
the University's objective of excellence in research, scholarship, and education
by publishing worldwide in

Oxford New York

Auckland Cape Town Dar es Salaam Hong Kong Karachi Kuala Lumpur
Madrid Melbourne Mexico City Nairobi New Delhi Shanghai Taipei Toronto

With offices in

Argentina Austria Brazil Chile Czech Republic France Greece Guatemala
Hungary Italy Japan Poland Portugal Singapore South Korea Switzerland
Thailand Turkey Ukraine Vietnam

Oxford is a registered trade mark of Oxford University Press in the UK and in
certain other countries

British Library Cataloguing in Publication Data

Data available

ISBN: 978 0 19 913901 9

10 9 8 7 6 5 4 3 2 1

Printed and bound by Martins the Printers, Berwick upon Tweed, UK.

Paper used in the production of this book is a natural, recyclable product made
from wood grown in sustainable forests. The manufacturing process conforms
to the environmental regulations of the country of origin.

Acknowledgements
The publishers would like to thank the following for permission to reproduce
photographs: p6: David L. Moore Studio/Alamy; p31: Kuzma/Shutterstock;
p35: Julia Pivovarova/Shutterstock; p39: OUP; p46: Maxstockphoto/Shutterstock;
p47: Eric Thierry Berluteau.
Artwork by: Kessia Beverley Smith, Stefan Chabluk, Pulsar Studios, Matt Ward.
Cover photograph by Don Hammond/design Pics/Corbis

The authors and publishers would like to thank the following people for their
help and advice:

Nicola Lester (editor); Geneviève Talon (language consultant); Colette Thomson
and Andrew Garrett at Footstep Productions (audio recordings).

Every effort has been made to contact copyright holders of material reproduced
in this book. If notified, the publishers will be pleased to rectify any errors or
omissions at the earliest opportunity.

Contents

Preparing for your GCSE   4

- How to get a good grade   4
- Preparing for the listening exam   5
- Preparing for the speaking controlled assessment   6
- Preparing for the reading exam   7
- Preparing for the writing controlled assessment   8

Pronunciation   9

Listening practice   11

Vocabulary in practice   17

Worksheets

- Unit 1A En forme   26
- Unit 1B Vivre ensemble   30
- Unit 2A Passe-temps et médias   34
- Unit 2B Voyages et vacances   38
- Unit 3A Chez moi et aux alentours   42
- Unit 3B Notre monde   46
- Unit 4A La vie à l'école   50
- Unit 4B Gagner sa vie   54

Answers   58

Notes   63

CD track list   64

Contents of CD

Audio tracks

- Audio tracks from Pronunciation section
- Audio tracks from Listening practice section

Preparing for your GCSE

How to get a good grade

1 Be organised

This workbook will help you make sure that you get the best possible grade in your GCSE.

- Spend time efficiently on activities that will really make a difference. Set yourself targets and keep working towards them.
- Get to know useful sections of the Students' Book and use them to check that your work is accurate.
- If your notes are untidy, put some time and effort into writing them up neatly. Sometimes charts or spider diagrams (also called 'mind maps') are as useful as lengthy notes.

2 Know your vocabulary

Words are the foundation of a language, so try to build up your French vocabulary.

- Try out different techniques for learning new words and phrases and see which ones work best for you. For example, you could use cards or pictures, write out topic or alphabetical lists, highlight tricky words or record yourself speaking.
- Pick out the most important words to learn for each topic, and concentrate on learning them well. The exam board prints a list of important vocabulary that you need to know – ask your teacher about it.
- Teach a friend or family member some French phrases, or get them to test you.
- Go back over vocabulary from previous units and keep using it.

3 Know your grammar

You need to know how French works in order to fit the words together. Once you've learnt a grammar point, it can be re-used with any topic.

- Read the *Grammaire* panels and the *Grammaire active* pages for each unit in the Students' Book. If there are points you don't understand, ask your teacher to explain.
- Make sure that you can recognise and form verbs. You need to get the person and the tense of the verb right. Can you talk about the past, present and future?
- Check that you can give opinions, add description and use linking words to make sentences more impressive.

4 Find out about France

- Take an interest in French personalities, food, music and culture.
- Read French magazines (for example, *Okapi, Le Monde des Ados* or *Géo Ados*) or look at French Internet sites. You could google key words using www.google.fr.

5 Show what you know

- Find out what knowledge and skills you need to show in Listening, Speaking, Reading and Writing, and check that you can do so. (See the tips on pages 5–8 of this book.)
- Make a revision timetable so you don't leave everything until the last minute. Make sure you cover each aspect: listening, speaking, reading and writing.
- Prepare for the exam by practising past papers. That way you will know the types of question to expect.

Preparing for the listening exam

1 Practice makes perfect
In listening exercises, you must be able to turn the sounds you hear into a word or phrase in your head.
* Read through transcripts as you listen, where possible.
* Revise sound-spelling links (see page 9).
* Tune your ear by listening to the CD that comes with this workbook as often as you can.

2 Before listening
The Listening exam accounts for 20% of your overall marks. At Foundation, your exam will last 30 minutes, plus 5 minutes reading time. Use the time wisely!
* Make the most of clues in the title, pictures or introduction.
* Read the instructions and questions carefully.
* Use the questions to help you focus. If there is a choice of answers or pictures to tick, think about which one or two words will give away the answer.
* Look carefully at the difference between the possible answers. If the choice is 700, 800 or 900, you don't need to be worried by the 100s. Focus on whether you hear 7, 8 or 9.

3 When listening
What you hear will always make sense and be logical. There won't be any tricks or catches.
* If the answer is a single word or short phrase, try writing down the sound you hear to try to turn it into a word you can recognise.
* With longer answers, listen all the way through, and never give up. One key word can give away the answer.
* Listen out for verbs, negatives, numbers and opinions.
* Concentrate on what you do understand, rather than on what you don't.

4 After listening
* Always listen twice and check your answers.
* Don't leave questions unanswered – make a sensible guess if necessary.

Listening is easy: they tell you the answers! But they just tell you in French!

Preparing for the speaking controlled assessment

1 Take control
It is up to you what you say, so make sure you equip yourself for the task.
- Be prepared to give opinions as well as information.
- If you know how to talk about the past or future, find ways to show off what you can do.

2 Get speaking
- Build your confidence. Get used to speaking French with a partner. If you can, record yourself to check your pronunciation. (If you get used to being filmed or recorded, it won't bother you in your assessed task.)
- Learn key phrases and vocabulary for the topic of the task you are doing.
- Build up a stock of French language that is useful for a range of topics.
- Build up routines that keep you talking, for example: opinion > reason > example.
- Use linking words to extend your answers: *et, mais, parce que*, etc.
- Use your answers to show off what you can do.

3 Preparing the task
You will be assessed on two tasks, both equally important. You will have time to prepare.
- Discuss the task and how to approach it with your teacher. They cannot tell you the French, but can help confirm the type of language you might need.
- Use all your reference materials to prepare the task.
- Make a plan (no more than 40 words) using the Task Planning Form your teacher will give you. Use bullet points and jot down prompt words – no full sentences or conjugated verbs. You can use pictures too.
- Make sure you get your message across, but don't forget to show off your French!

4 The assessment task
Each task will last between 4 and 6 minutes and will be filmed or recorded, and then the film or recording will be sent to the exam board so that the grade you have been awarded can be checked.
- You are allowed to take in your notes (see above).
- Listen carefully to the questions. Most of the French will be familiar to you.
- Ask (in French) if you want a question repeated. You won't lose marks for doing so, and it is better to understand fully.
- There may be one or two unexpected questions, but they are not there to trip you up. Just think of a simple, logical way to react.
- Concentrate on getting your message across.
- If you can, use linking words and opinions, reasons or examples to help you keep speaking until you are asked the next question.

Preparing for the reading exam

Put the tips and strategies on this page into practice when you work on the *Lecture* pages in your Students' Book.

1 Before reading

I wonder what this text is about?

- Reading is much easier when you have a good knowledge of vocabulary, so learn and revise as many words as you can, particularly those from the exam board's vocabulary list.
- When you see a text for the first time, use all available clues, such as the title, introduction and illustrations, to help you work out what the text is about.
- Read the instructions carefully to find out exactly what you are meant to do. (If the text is on one page and the questions are on the next, don't be caught out by looking only at one page!)
- Read the questions, because they give more clues about the content of the text and tell you what to look for in it.

2 When reading

- Start by reading the text right through quickly, to get an overall understanding. Then read it again, concentrating on the information you need to answer the questions.
- Remember that the answers appear in the text in the same order as the questions, except for the answers to summary questions about the whole text.
- There won't be any tricks or catches in the exam paper, but watch out for details that seem to be hiding, such as the date at the top of a letter or the person's name at the end.
- No dictionaries are allowed in the exam. But even if you don't understand every word, you can use what you do know to make sense of the text.
- Use strategies you have learnt to work out the meaning of unfamiliar words. For example:
  - ♦ Are they like English words? (e.g. *recommande* – recommend, *une erreur* – error, *la cantine* – canteen)
  - ♦ Are they similar to any French words you do know? (e.g. *un collégien* – *le collège*, *un voyageur* – *un voyage*, *orageux* – *un orage*)
  - ♦ Is there a prefix or suffix which can help you work out the meaning? (e.g. *improbable* – *probable*, *une gendarmerie* – *un gendarme*)
- If you have to answer in English, keep your answer close to what the French says, to show that you are not just guessing.
- Put a sensible answer to each question.
- Keep answers brief. The amount of space given for you to write in and the number of marks for a question are clues about how much to write. You won't get 4 marks for just writing a single word, but there is no point in writing a lot if there is only a short line for writing the answer and only a single mark is allocated to the question.

Preparing for the writing controlled assessment

1 Aiming for a good grade

Each piece of writing will focus on a different format or purpose. To achieve a good grade, you must be able to:
- give information
- give opinions
- talk about the past, present and future.

2 Preparing the task

You will have time to prepare the task, using reference materials. Make a plan (no more than 40 words) using the Task Planning Sheet your teacher will give you. Use bullet points and jot down prompt words – no full sentences or conjugated verbs, but you can jot down infinitives. Your teacher can discuss the task with you, but must not help you with the French. Write a draft copy making sure that:
- you plan and organise your ideas
- your writing is in the right format (letter, magazine article, etc.)
- you do everything the task asks for
- you manage to show off the French you know.

3 The assessment task

When you are writing up the final version, you can use your Task Planning Sheet and a dictionary. You will **not** have access to your draft copy, nor to online spellcheckers or translators if you are word-processing your task.
- Write in proper sentences and paragraphs, using words and phrases that you know.
- Use your notes to make sure you include all the ideas and language you need to achieve a good grade.
- Keep an eye on the time. You will have one hour to write up to 200 words. For grades G–D: you must write 200-350 words **across the two tasks** (400-600 for grade C and above).
- Leave time at the end for checking your work.

4 Checking your work

Check your work several times, looking at different features each time:
- gender and agreement (masculine, feminine and plural nouns and adjectives)
- verbs: tense, person/endings
- spelling and accents.

Tu veux un rat blanc ou une souris blanche?

Don't forget that adjectives need to agree with the nouns they describe!

Pronunciation

Vowels

1 **French vowel sounds are brisk and simple** 🎙 *Track 2*
Read out these phrases. Then listen to the recording of them on the CD, to check your pronunciation.

a	C'est un ananas
e	J'aime les cerises
i, y	Il y a des kiwis
o	Un gros abricot
u	Le jus de prune

2 **Accents on *e* change the way it sounds** 🎙 *Track 3*
Read out these words and the sentence that includes them all. Then listen to the recording to check your pronunciation.

e	petit
é	bébé
è	mère
ë	Noël
ê	fête

À Noël, c'est la fête du petit bébé et de sa mère.

3 **Vowels together can make new sounds** 🎙 *Track 4*
Read out these sentences. Then check your pronunciation by listening to the recording.

ai = ei	J'aime la neige.
oi	Le roi, c'est moi!
ou = où	Où est le chou?
ui	C'est pour lui.
oui	Louis a dit oui.

4 **Vowels followed by *n* or *m* make nasal sounds** 🎙 *Track 5*
'Nasal' sounds are made through the nose. Read out these sentences. Then listen to the recording to check your pronunciation.

am, an, en, em	Ambre a un an en décembre.
in, aim, ein, ain	Le lapin a faim et mange plein de pain.
un	C'est un grand brun.
on, om	Dis ton nom et ton prénom.
oin	C'est dans le coin? Non, c'est loin.

5 **The vowel *e* followed by *r*, *t* or *z* sounds like *é* or *è*** 🎙 *Track 6*
Read out these sentences. Then listen to the recording to check your pronunciation.

er = et = ez (sounds like é)	Le boucher et le boulanger ont un gros nez.
et (sounds like è)	C'est un alphabet secret.

Consonants

6 **French consonants sound mostly like English ones, with a few differences**   🔊 *Track 7*
Read out these phrases and sentences. Then listen to the recording to check your pronunciation.

c sounds like **k**, or like **s** before **e**, **i** and **y** **ç** sounds like **s** before **a**, **o** and **u** **ch** sounds like **sh**, not **tch**	Un clafoutis aux cerises. Un garçon français. Va chercher les chips!
g sounds like **g**, or like **j** before **e**, **i** and **y** **gn** sounds like **nye** (as in 'canyon')	Ginette est à la gare de Boulogne.
h is always silent (as in 'hour')	Hourra!
j sounds a bit like **zh**	J'aime ce jeu.
qu sounds like **k** (as in 'quiche')	C'est qui?
r sounds like **rrr** (quite raspy)	Mon frère regarde la mer.
s sounds like **s**, or like **z** between two vowels	Les Russes aiment les roses.
th = **t** (as in Thomas); **tion** = **ss** (not **sh**)	Un thé après la natation.

7 **Consonants at the end of words are not usually pronounced, but these sometimes are: b, d, g, m, n, p, s, t, x, z**   🔊 *Track 8*
Read out the following phrases. Then listen to the recording to check your pronunciation. (The consonants in pale type are not pronounced.)

d	Il fait froid.
g	C'est long!
m	Quel parfum?
n	Il a un examen.
p	J'aime beaucoup ça.

s	Trois fois.
t	Il dit salut!
x	Dis le prix!
z	C'est du riz.

8 **Usually, c, r, f and l at the end of a word are pronounced**   🔊 *Track 9*
You can remember the letters by thinking: CaReFuL! Some exceptions are shown in the chart below. Read out these sentences. Then listen to the recording to check your pronunciation.

c (and also **k** and **q**)	Il part avec cinq anoraks.
r (except words ending in 'er' and 'ier')	J'apprends par cœur.
f	Le chef est actif.
l (except words ending in 'ail' and 'eil')	L'hôtel ouvre en avril.

9 **At the end of words, d, n, s, t, x and z are silent, unless the next word begins with a vowel**   🔊 *Track 10*
Read out these phrases. Then listen to the recording to check your pronunciation. The linking of the consonant to the vowel at the start of the next word is called a 'liaison'. The letters in brackets show what the consonant sounds like in the liaison.

un grand ami [t]   un petit ami [t]   mon ami [n]

mes amis [z]   de vieux amis [z]   chez elle [z]

There is some extra pronunciation practice material on the CD.   🔊 *Track 11*

Listening practice

Exercises 1–8 below are similar to the listening exercises you will do for the exam. The recordings are on the CD, and transcripts are on pages 15–16.

The total mark you can achieve for these exercises is 35. Good luck!

1 Hobbies

Track 12

Which hobby does each person have?

Example: playing football

1 _Going to the cinema_ (1 mark)

2 _Playing video games_ (1 mark)

3 _Going out at the weekend with friends_ (1 mark)

4 _To play music_ (1 mark)

2 Family

Track 13

Which family is each person describing?
Write the correct letter in each box.

A

B

C

D

E

F

Example: F

5 D (1 mark)

6 E (1 mark)

7 A (1 mark)

8 C (1 mark)

3 Food

Write the correct letter in the box and say why Anya chose those things for the dinner she prepared for friends.

Write 1 because it's healthy
Write 2 because she loves it
Write 3 because she is vegetarian

A B  C

D E F

Example	B	1
9	A	1
10	C	3
11	F	2

(2 marks)
(2 marks)
(2 marks)

4 Étienne and Lianne speak about where they live.
Track 15

12 Étienne lives in ...

A B  C

Write the correct letter in the box. A (1 mark)

13 Lianne doesn't live in ...

A B C

Write the correct letter in the box. A (1 mark)

14 Étienne's village is ...

A B C

Write the correct letter in the box. B (1 mark)

15 In Paris, Lianne likes ...

A   **B**   **C**

Write the correct letter in the box. [C]   (1 mark)

16 Étienne goes shopping by ...

A   **B**   **C**

Write the correct letter in the box. [C]   (1 mark)

5 Sporty living

Track 16

Complete this form with the required information.

Example: Name: Hugo

17 Number of hours of PE at school: _2 hours a week_ (1 mark)

18 Sport he doesn't like in PE: _gymnastic_ (1 mark)

19 Sport he plays in a club: _danse_ (1 mark)

20 Sport he does on Sunday: _jogging_ (1 mark)

6 Problems for young people

Track 17

Fill in the grid.

	Name	Concern	Suggested solution	
Example:	Malika	dangers of alcohol	talk about the dangers in primary school	
21	Nathan	Study	The possibilities of working practically to get an idea of what it's like working in the world	(2 marks)
22	Nina	Pollution in nature	Lessons at school on how to protect the planet.	(2 marks)

7 Free time

Track 18

23 When he got injured, Théo was …

A	watching football.
B	playing football.
c	volunteering at hospital.

Write the correct letter in the box. B   (1 mark)

24 Margaux was …

A	shopping for clothes.
B	helping in a shop.
c	making some clothes.

Write the correct letter in the box. C   (1 mark)

25 Last night, Alexis saw …

A	a play at the theatre.
B	a film at the cinema.
c	a film on DVD.

Write the correct letter in the box. C   (1 mark)

26 This morning, Marion …

A	went to the gym.
B	ran with a friend.
c	did leg exercises.

Write the correct letter in the box. B   (1 mark)

8 Portrait

Track 19

A	age and birthday
B	hobby
C	hair
D	helping at home
E	family and pet
F	holidays

What is Luc Garnier talking about? Write the correct letter in each box.

Example: A

27 C   (1 mark)

28 E   (1 mark)

29 B   (1 mark)

30 D   (1 mark)

Transcripts

Exercise 1 🎵 *Track 12*
Example: Moi, je joue au football deux fois par semaine.

1 Mon passe-temps préféré, c'est aller au cinéma.
2 J'aime jouer à des jeux vidéo sur ma console.
3 J'aime surtout sortir le week-end avec des copains.
4 Ce que je préfère, c'est jouer de la musique. Je suis dans un groupe.

Exercise 2 🎵 *Track 13*
Example: Dans ma famille, il y a mon père, mon petit frère et moi.

5 Je suis fille unique et j'habite avec ma mère.
6 Chez moi, il y a ma mère, mon beau-père et ma grand-mère.
7 J'ai un petit frère et une petite sœur qui sont jumeaux.
8 Dans ma famille, il y a moi, et il y a aussi mon grand frère et mes parents.

Exercise 3 🎵 *Track 14*
9 Comme entrée, j'ai fait une soupe de légumes, avec des pommes de terre, des oignons et des carottes parce que les légumes, c'est excellent pour la santé et ça ne fait pas grossir!
10 Comme plat principal, j'ai fait des spaghettis avec une sauce tomate parce que je suis végétarienne. Je ne mange jamais de viande ni de poisson, ou en tout cas très rarement du poisson.
11 Comme dessert, je voulais faire une tarte aux fruits mais je n'avais pas assez de sucre! Alors j'ai fait un dessert simple mais que j'adore, une salade de fruits. C'est mon dessert préféré, je crois.

Exercise 4 🎵 *Track 15*
12 *Boy:* Salut! Moi, je m'appelle Étienne. J'habite dans un petit village. Et toi?

13 *Girl:* Moi, j'habite à Paris quand je suis avec ma mère et dans la banlieue quand je suis avec mon père.
[Pause]
14 *Boy:* Moi, j'aime bien mon village parce qu'il est historique et très pittoresque.
Girl: Moi, je n'aimerais pas habiter dans un village, c'est trop calme.
[Pause]
15 *Boy:* Et Paris, c'est bien? Qu'est-ce que tu aimes là-bas?
Girl: Eh bien, il y a beaucoup de magasins et beaucoup de cinémas.
[Pause]
16 *Boy:* Les magasins et les cinémas sont à 25 kilomètres de mon village, dans un grand centre commercial.
Girl: Oh, c'est loin!
Boy: On peut y aller en bus. C'est assez rapide.
Girl: Tu y vas souvent?
Boy: J'y vais environ une fois par mois, avec des copains.

Exercise 5 🎵 *Track 16*
Example: Salut! C'est Hugo. Je suis très sportif et je vais te parler de ce que je fais pour être en forme.
[Pause]
17 D'abord, je fais de l'éducation physique au lycée deux fois par semaine, une heure le lundi et deux heures le vendredi.
[Pause]
18 Au lycée, j'aime surtout les jeux d'équipe, comme le basket-ball et le handball qui est mon sport préféré. Par contre, la gymnastique, ça ne m'intéresse pas.
[Pause]

19 Je joue au handball dans un club. Je m'entraîne avec l'équipe le mardi soir et je joue des matchs le samedi après-midi.

[Pause]

20 Le dimanche matin, je fais deux heures de jogging. Je n'aime pas beaucoup ça, et c'est dur, mais c'est bon pour la forme! Voilà!

Exercise 6   🔊 *Track 17*

Example: Malika

Ce qui m'inquiète, c'est les jeunes qui boivent trop. L'alcool, c'est tellement dangereux! À mon avis, on devrait parler des dangers de l'alcool aux enfants à l'école primaire, avant qu'ils prennent de mauvaises habitudes.

21 Nathan

Je pense que pour certains, comme moi, les études, ce n'est pas très motivant. Les lycéens devraient avoir la possibilité de faire plus de stages pratiques, pour avoir une meilleure idée du monde du travail.

22 Nina

Le plus horrible pour moi, c'est la pollution de la nature. On est en train d'abîmer la planète. Si on ne fait rien, ce sera trop tard! Il devrait y avoir des cours d'écologie à l'école. Comme ça on apprendrait à protéger la planète.

Exercise 7   🔊 *Track 18*

23 Théo

Je jouais au football... Tout d'un coup, j'ai eu très mal au pied... et... je ne pouvais plus marcher! On m'a emmené à l'hôpital en ambulance.

24 Margaux

Je l'ai vue dans la vitrine! J'en ai essayé deux autres, mais j'ai pris celle-ci. Elle n'était pas trop chère et c'est juste ma taille.

25 Alexis

C'était vraiment nul! Les acteurs ne jouaient pas bien et l'histoire n'était vraiment pas intéressante. Je ne le recommanderai à personne! Attendez la sortie en DVD!

26 Marion

J'ai fait du jogging avec une copine ce matin. C'est dur pour les jambes mais je dois faire quelque chose pour être plus en forme!

Exercise 8   🔊 *Track 19*

Example: Salut! Je m'appelle Luc Garnier. J'ai 15 ans. Mon anniversaire, c'est le 18 février.

27 Je suis blond et mes cheveux sont longs et bouclés.

28 J'ai trois sœurs et deux petits frères. Mes parents sont divorcés et j'habite avec ma mère. Nous avons un chien qui s'appelle Filou.

29 Mon passe-temps préféré, c'est regarder la télé.

30 À la maison, je fais souvent la vaisselle mais je déteste ranger mes affaires!

Vocabulary in practice

Building up your vocabulary

The ideas and activities on pages 17–25 will give you skills and strategies you can use to build up your French vocabulary.

Keeping a personal record

To build a stock of vocabulary, keep a record of all the useful language you meet. Keep a personal vocabulary file, organised alphabetically, by topic or in some other way that is meaningful to you.

Memorising new words and phrases

To help you memorise a new word or phrase, you could:

- ☐ read it over and over
- ☐ repeat it over and over in your head or aloud
- ☐ record yourself saying it and listen back
- ☐ spell it, silently or aloud
- ☐ find a link between the new word or phrase and something you already know (for example, if you already know *ouvert*, that might help you to remember *les horaires d'**ouvert**ure*)
- ☐ draw a spider diagram (mind map) of words that are linked in some way

- ☐ invent a mime or visual image
- ☐ write the word out ten times
- ☐ write a sentence using it
- ☐ write it on a post-it note and stick this somewhere where you will see it often
- ☐ make up a rap or jingle using it
- ☐ write it on a small card with the English translation on the back and use it to test yourself
- ☐ ask a friend or relative to test you.

Write a new word or phrase on a post-it and stick it somewhere where you will see it often.

Tick off the strategies above as you try them. We all learn in different ways. Which ones work best for you?

Learning nouns and adjectives

Deciding which words to learn

1 Write the French equivalents of these English words. Check page 46 of the Students' Book. Then mark the words as follows:

Tick = I already know it
Underline = I could have guessed it
Circle = I need to learn this word

a *shy* _____

b *stubborn* _____

c *funny* _____

d *a shower* _____

e *a half brother* _____

f *atmosphere* _____

g *happy* _____

h *hard-working* _____

i *a teenager* _____

j *theft* _____

2 Check the meaning of the words in the box below. They are all on page 82 of the Students' Book. Underline the five that you would learn first for the topic 'My holiday'. Circle any words that you think might be the examiner's favourites – ones you need to learn because you could never guess what they mean.

la natation	une chambre	la plage	la piscine
les vacances	un hôtel	un camping	un parc d'attractions

3 Grouping words can be helpful. Check the meaning of these words on page 118 of the Students' Book. Put them into two groups to help you learn them.

le car	les transports en commun	les déchets	la poubelle
le métro	recyclé les emballages	le tramway	la marche à pied
le chauffage			

4 Look at the vocabulary page for unit 4A or 4B in your Students' Book. Use one of the activities above to help you focus on the words to learn.

Using different strategies for learning

5 Pictures can help you to remember vocabulary. Use these words to label the picture below.

> l'avion   le balcon   la douche   l'hôtel   le lit   le nuage   la piscine   le soleil

6 Check the meaning of these words on page 82 of the Students' Book: *une douche, une église, un avion, une île*. Then draw pictures on a sheet of paper to help you remember the words. Symbols or stick people will do!

7 To help you remember a word, use any clue that is in the word itself. It may be similar to another word you know in French or in English. For example:

word	clue	meaning
un vendeur	vend = *sells*	*salesperson*

Write the clues to the meanings, and then the meanings, of these words.

word	clue(s)	meaning
un ouvre-bouteille		
une poissonnerie		
la politesse		

8 Learn by writing. Carefully copy the French words below in a list down the side of a piece of paper. Then write the English meanings of the words in another column next to the French ones. (Check the meanings on page 64 of the Students' Book.) Fold the French words away so that you are looking at just the English words. Try to write the French words correctly in a third column. Open out the paper and check your spellings. Carry on across the page, until you can spell all the words.

> la danse   la musique   la randonnée   un passe-temps
> un jeu électronique   un avantage   un inconvénient

9 Try out strategies 5–8 for the vocabulary you are learning or revising. Evaluate which strategies have the most impact for you.

Learning verbs

Noticing verbs

Don't make the mistake of just learning nouns!

1 Underline all the verbs in this box.

j'ai   projets   allez   descendre   avoir   vélo   ensuite
d'abord   tu vois   impossible   on est

2 Look at the vocabulary page in the Students' Book for the unit you are studying or revising. How many of the words on the page are verbs?

Organising your learning

Learn verbs in the infinitive (the form in which they appear in dictionaries and word lists).

3 Draw arrows to match each verb in the left-hand column to its infinitive in the right-hand column.

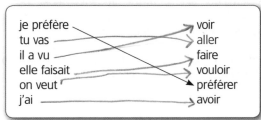

je préfère   voir
tu vas   aller
il a vu   faire
elle faisait   vouloir
on veut   préférer
j'ai   avoir

4 You need to know which verbs are not regular. You can check this by looking at the verb tables at the back of the Students' Book. Write the following infinitives in the correct column below and put the English in brackets beside them. The first one has been done for you.

avoir ✓   aimer ✓   parler ✓   faire ✓   voir ✓
être ✓   finir ✓   écouter ✓   ? chanter ✓   aller ✓

REGULAR	IRREGULAR
aimer (to like)	avoir (to have)
finir (to finish)	être (to be)
parler (to speak)	aller (to go)
faire (to do/make)	voir (to see)
chanter (to sing)	

5 Keep a list of useful verbs for each separate topic, plus a list of verbs that will always be useful for any topic. Which lists would you put these verbs in?

manger   aider   déjeuner   faire   avoir   boire   prendre
goûter   ajouter   cuisiner

Example: Food and drink: *manger*, ... Any topic: *aider*, ...

Targeted learning
These are the top 6 most commonly used verbs in French:

1 avoir
2 faire
3 être
4 dire
5 aller
6 voir

More useful irregular verbs it is helpful to know:
savoir: je sais, etc.
pouvoir: je peux, etc.
falloir: il faut, etc.
vouloir: je veux, etc.

You will need to be aware of all the different forms of these verbs. They are **all** irregular so you will need to learn by heart the different forms of each one.
Example: for *avoir*:

Present:
j'ai   nous avons
tu as   vous avez
il/elle/on a   ils/elles ont
Perfect: j'ai eu, tu as eu, etc.
Future: j'aurai, tu auras, etc.

6 To learn the verb forms, try the strategies below and then grade how useful you found each one:
1 = I'll definitely try this again
2 = I'll probably try this again
3 = I might try this again

a Write the verb out, then read it aloud. That way you are writing, reading, speaking and listening! ☐

b Choose a text. For each verb you read, say or write out other forms of the verb. For example, if you read: *elle est*, you say: *je suis, tu es, il/elle/on est, nous sommes, vous êtes, ils/elles sont.* ☐

c Work with a partner to test each other. Write a list of 10 infinitives. A chooses a verb, B challenges him/her to give a form, e.g. perfect tense, 2nd person plural. ☐

d Make up a verb quiz. Write out questions on one side of a card.
Example:
1 aller: perfect tense with 'elle'?

Use the verb tables in your Students' Book or dictionary to check the answers and write them on the back of the card.
Example:
1 elle est allée

A week later see if you can answer the questions without looking at the answers. ☐

e Set the verb conjugation to a well-known tune. Sing it in the shower or as you cycle to school! ☐

7 Now try the activities in the *AQA GCSE French Grammar Workbook*, which provide further practice on verbs in all their many different forms.

Revising high-frequency words

When learning vocabulary, keep a separate list of words that are useful for any topic. Revise these words as often as you can.

Little words

Watch out for expressions where the 'little' words are slightly different in French and English.

1 Match the French to the English.

un	*the* (plural)
une	*of* or *from the* (feminine)
des	*to the* (plural)
le	*a* (feminine)
la	*of the* (masculine)
les	*a* (masculine)
de	*of* or *from*
de la	*the* (masculine)
du	*the* (feminine)
à	*at* or *to*
au ⟶	*to the* (masculine)
aux	(*of*) *the* (plural)

2 On a separate sheet, translate sentences **a–e** literally, and then into correct English.

Example: Je joue au football. = *I play at the football.* = *I play football.*

a J'aime les animaux.

b Je dors dans la chambre de mon frère.

c Je vais au lycée le samedi.

d Il est prof de maths.

e J'ai mal à la jambe.

Connectives

Using extended sentences will earn you marks in the exam. You can make your sentences longer by adding information, using the right connectives.

3 Find the correct French linking words from this list to write next to their English equivalents below. The first one has been done for you.

après ✓	avant	d'abord	et	mais
parce que	par exemple	puis		

after	après	*but*		
and		*first*		
because		*for instance*		
before		*then*		

4 Use connectives from activity 3 to fill in the gaps in these sentences about a famous French slam poet.

a ___Avant___ son accident, il s'appelait Fabien Marsaud. _____ son accident, il a choisi le nom de Grand Corps Malade.

b Il a choisi ce nom _____ il est très grand et il est handicapé.

c Il fait du slam. _____ il slamme dans les bars de Paris, _____ il devient célèbre dans toute la France.

Time words

You are more likely to get a good grade, in Listening, Speaking, Reading and Writing, if you are able to understand and refer to different time frames.

5 Circle the time words and phrases below in different colours to show whether they refer to the past, the present or the future. Use black for past, red for present and blue for future. Copy the words onto a separate sheet and write the English equivalent beside each one.

> maintenant   hier   aujourd'hui   demain   la semaine prochaine
> la semaine dernière   plus tard   avant   en ce moment

6 Choose time words from activity 5 to fill in the gaps in these sentences. Several answers are possible for each one.

a _____ j'ai mal à la tête.

b On est allé en France _____.

c Est-ce que tu veux aller au cinéma _____?

Question words

To answer correctly in the exam, you need to be able to understand the questions!

7 Complete these French question words.

who?	qu_____	why?	po_____
when?	qu_____	how?	co_____
how much/many?	co_____	which?	qu_____
where?	o_____	what?	qu'e_____

8 Use the correct word to start each of these questions. Then write answers in French on a separate sheet.

a ___Où___ habites-tu?

b _____ fais-tu du sport?

c _____ vas-tu au lycée?

d _____ d'argent de poche as-tu chaque mois?

e _____ tu aimes faire le week-end?

f _____ admires-tu le plus?

Learning expressions and structures

Some expressions are not topic-based and will be useful in any context. Keep a record of them and revise them regularly.

Expressing your opinion

In the exam, you will improve your marks by saying what you think or feel and expressing your opinions.

1 Read these opinion phrases. Circle the positive ones and underline the negative ones.

> je déteste   ça m'énerve
>
>   j'aime   je préfère
>
> ça m'intéresse   ça ne me plaît pas

2 Choose words from this box that are (a) positive and (b) negative, and use them in the sentences below.

> intéressant   ennuyeux   injuste   génial
>
> sympa   nul   inutile   passionnant

Example: Pour moi, c'est (a) génial (b) ennuyeux

Pour moi, c'est (a) _____ (b) _____

Je trouve ça (a) _____ (b) _____

À mon avis, c'est (a) _____ (b) _____

Je pense que c'est (a) _____ (b) _____

3 On a separate sheet, write your personal opinion about the following subjects, using as many phrases from activities 1 and 2 as you can.

Example: J'aime/Je déteste les voyages à l'étranger.

les voyages à l'étranger   les devoirs

l'éducation physique   l'uniforme scolaire

la pollution

Talking about the future

The examiner is likely to ask you about your future plans. Using a variety of phrases will give you a better grade.

4 Match the English to the French phrases.

> | | |
> |---|---|
> | *I'm going to* | je veux |
> | *I want to* | je vais |
> | *I would like to* | j'espère |
> | *I intend to* | j'aimerais |
> | *I hope to* | j'ai l'intention de |

5 Practise using phrases from activity 4 to fill in the gaps in sentences a–c. (There are several possible answers for each gap.) Write out the sentences on a separate sheet.

a Si j'ai de bonnes notes, *** aller au lycée parce que *** continuer mes études.

b Quand j'aurai 18 ans, *** partir habiter à l'étranger pendant un an parce que je *** de voyager.

c Dans 10 ans *** être prof de langues parce que *** enseigner les langues aux enfants de l'école primaire.

Making descriptions more precise

Be sure to learn and use some intensifiers (the little words that go in front of adjectives) in your descriptions.

Example: *Il faisait **assez** froid et j'étais **vraiment** fatigué(e).* – It was **quite** cold and I was **really** tired.

6 Match the French and English words.

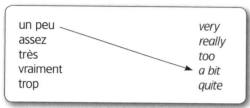

un peu	very
assez	really
très	too
vraiment	a bit
trop	quite

7 Write these sentences on a separate sheet, adding a different intensifier in each.

Example: *Il fait beau. > Il fait très beau.*

a Je suis organisé et responsable.

b Le prof est sévère mais juste.

c Le film était ennuyeux.

d Les DVD ne sont pas chers.

e J'ai lu un livre intéressant.

Giving your reasons

Learn how to explain/justify what you say. Pick out useful words from the sentences in activity 8.

8 Fill in the grid by matching the beginnings and endings of these six statements.

1 J'aime bien mon collège   a pour me relaxer.

2 J'écoute de la musique   b parce que les profs sont sympa.

3 Je ne sors pas   c car c'est mauvais pour la santé.

4 Je ne fume pas   d comme il pleut.

5 Je fais du sport   e pour aller sur Internet.

6 Mon ordinateur est important   f parce que je suis sportif.

Example: *J'aime bien mon collège parce que les profs sont sympa.*

1	2	3	4	5	6
b					

9 Write different endings for the sentences in activity 8.

Example: *J'aime bien mon collège parce qu'il y a une bonne ambiance.*

Unit 1A En forme

Controlled Assessment: Speaking

Students' Book pages 24–25

You are going to have a conversation with your teacher about healthy lifestyle.

Preparing the task

1 Prepare the task using your Students' Book. Use Unit 1A to make sure you have the necessary language for talking about healthy and unhealthy lifestyles:

pages 12–13 = about sport and sporting activities
pages 14–15 = about possible pros and cons of exercising
pages 16–17 = about healthy cooking
pages 18–19 = about good and bad habits, including alcohol
pages 20–21 = about making healthy resolutions happen

2 Research well and plan what you want to say. You are allowed to make notes which you can then take with you when performing the task in the Controlled Assessment: no more than 40 words, with no conjugated verbs.

3 Practise the conversation using your notes. Try to avoid saying everything in the same way and using the same vocabulary and structures. You may want to memorise some facts in order to feel more secure during the exam but leave the wording flexible. Have a go at speaking from these notes:

* *alimentation équilibrée, végétarien(ne) mais frites*
* *sport:-(mais exercice: tennis, badminton avec copines, danse samedi*
* *bonnes habitudes: bien manger, dormir mais mauvaises: fumer un peu et alcool*
* *résolutions: arrêter de fumer, plus d'exercice: parcours-santé dimanche*

4 In the exam, you will be asked a question or two which you will not have covered in your notes. This does not mean that you can't prepare for it: try to predict what your teacher might ask you and work out possible answers.

Performing the task

1 It will be better if your replies to your teacher's questions sound natural rather than scripted and learnt by heart.
Remember to use "conversational tools" like "*Alors ... Eh bien ... Euh ...*"

2 You'll be assessed on "Communication", which means the amount of information and ideas you present.
For a good grade in the speaking assessment, make sure you develop your answers as fully as possible and give your own point of view on the issues.

Controlled Assessment: Writing

Students' Book pages 26–27

A French magazine is asking young people to present their favourite sports personality for the 'Top Ten Sports Personality Award'. Choose yours and write a text explaining why you think he/she should be included in the Top Ten.

Preparing the task

1 Use the Internet to research details of the sportsperson you want to put forward. You could use a mind map to plan your research and record your findings.

Example:

2 Prepare the task using your Students' Book to revise the language and the grammar you will need to complete the task. Here in particular, you will need to use the perfect tense to describe actions which took place in the past.

Refer to *Grammaire active*, page 23 in your Students' Book.

He/She was born ...   He/She started ...   He/She won ...

He/She became ..., etc.

3 Draft and redraft to make sure you are happy with the content of your text. Try to fit the content around what you know how to say, apart from very specific or technical vocabulary you can't avoid and which you can look up in a dictionary.

4 In the final writing assessment, you are allowed to take with you a plan of up to **40 words maximum** (no conjugated verbs), in French or English. Prepare this carefully as it must trigger your memory for content and language.

Writing the task

1 This is not the time to start improvising or developing new ideas. Stick with what you planned and show off your knowledge of French! Don't be tempted to use a dictionary. Only use it as a last resort or to check a spelling, if you have the time.

2 You'll be assessed on "Content", which means the amount of information and ideas you provide. These have to be relevant to the task.

For a good grade in the writing assessment, you're expected not only to provide opinions but also to **explain your opinions**. Remember *parce que* and *car* will be your friends!

Grammaire active

Students' Book pages 22–23

> irregular and modal verbs ■ reflexive verbs ■ perfect tense ■ *du/de la/des*

1 In these questions and answers, fill in the endings of the irregular verbs.

Example: ils **fon** _____ = ils **font**

a Vous **appren** _____ le français au lycée?

 – Non, nous **fais** _____ italien.

b Tes cousins **vienn** _____ pendant les vacances?

 – Non, ils ne **peuv** _____ pas.

c Tu **sor** _____ avec nous samedi?

 – Non, je **doi** _____ aller à la piscine.

d Ton frère **veu** _____ venir au ciné avec nous ce soir?

 – Non, il **par** _____ en voyage ce soir.

2 Fill the gaps with the reflexive pronouns *me/m', te/t'* or *se/s'*.

a Le matin, je _me_ réveille tôt. Je ____ lève et je prends ma douche. J'aime bien ____ laver le matin.

b Mon frère n'aime pas ____ lever et il déteste ____ laver le matin, alors il ____ douche le soir.

c Mon frère et moi, on ____ entend bien. On fait nos devoirs ensemble et on ____ aide!

3 Use the verbs in the box to complete the grid below. Then write a sentence for each on a separate sheet.

> es allé   habitons   ont pris   prennent
> vas   finit   avons habité   a fini

	infinitive	present tense	perfect tense
-er:	habiter	habitons	
-ir:	finir		
-re:	prendre		
irreg.	aller		

4 Fill in the gaps in these sentences with *du, de la, de l', des, d'* or *de*.

a Tu veux _____ frites avec le steak?

b Tu as déjà fait _____ voile?

c Mes parents ne font pas assez _____ exercice.

d Je ne bois jamais _____ sodas.

e C'est une sauce avec _____ huile et _____ sauce tomate.

Checklist

Fill in the checklist according to how confident you feel.

Key

☺	I know/can do this very well
😐	I'm not too sure I know/can do this
☹	I don't know/cannot do this well enough

Unit 1A En forme	How confident am I?
I can **1** talk about sports and say which sports I do	
2 say why I do or don't do exercise	
3 discuss how to exercise safely	
4 talk about food and describe a recipe	
5 discuss healthy or unhealthy diet	
6 discuss the dangers of alcohol	
7 discuss the consequences of unhealthy lifestyles	
Skills **8** use determiners correctly	
9 make liaisons between words	
10 use tone of voice to sound convincing	
11 speak precisely using adverbs	
12 illustrate what I say with examples	
13 use descriptions and linking words to make longer sentences	
Grammar **14** use the present tense of regular and irregular verbs	
15 use reflexive verbs	
16 use the future tense with *aller* + infinitive	
17 use the perfect tense	
18 use adverbs of time (when) and manner (how)	
19 use *le, la, les/un, une, des* correctly	
20 use *du, de la, des* correctly	
21 recognise the pronoun *en*	

Unit 1B Vivre ensemble

Controlled Assessment: Speaking

🖉 Students' Book pages 42–43

You are going to invent a new personality and family for yourself for the virtual world of Second Life and then have a conversation with your teacher about it.

Preparing the task

1 Prepare the task using your Students' Book. Use Unit 1B to make sure you have the necessary language to speak about family members and their personalities:

pages 30–31 = describing someone's personality
pages 32–33 = family members and how you get along with them
pages 34–35 = future plans regarding marriage/changes in family life

Note down any words/expressions and tenses you find which will be useful for your conversation. See *Grammaire*, page 35 in your Students' Book, to revise how to talk about future plans.

2 Plan what you want to say. Build your answers around the questions on page 42 of the Students' Book.

3 Make notes on the sheet your teacher gives you. You can take this with you when you perform the task under controlled conditions: no more than 40 words, with no conjugated verbs, so just write verbs in the infinitive.

4 Practise using your notes. Try to sound natural. If you need time to think, pause and use fillers like: "*Euh ..., Alors ..., Eh bien ..., Bref ...*"
Practise aloud developing the notes below to say how you get on with family members and why:

> – père – ✗, sévère
> – mère – ✓, patiente
> – sœur – ✓✓, drôle, gentille

5 Don't forget to try and predict what unexpected question the teacher might ask you and work out possible answers.

Performing the task

1 Keep the conversation going, using your fillers if necessary.

2 Marks are awarded for "Interaction and fluency". This means you need to respond without too many hesitations and to keep the conversation going.
For a good grade in the speaking assessment, make sure you develop your answers. Avoid yes/no answers.

Controlled Assessment: Writing

Students' Book pages 44–45

Write a letter to the president of France about a social issue that concerns you.

Preparing the task

1 Decide which issue you want to talk about and use the Internet to research some facts and figures. You might feel more confident if you choose an issue you have worked on in class, like poverty.

2 Prepare the task using your Students' Book to revise the language and the grammar you will need to complete the task. Think about the type of language you will need to use to address a president: chatty or formal?

3 Write a rough draft. Although you are allowed to look up words you don't know in a dictionary at this stage, try to fit the content around what you know how to say, avoiding too much technical vocabulary.

4 Think about each part of the task. Double-check! Have you covered all the points? Have you used a variety of ways to say what you think and give your opinion?

Writing the task

1 Use your notes to make sure you have included everything you wanted to write. Keep an eye on the time. It is important to check your text once you have finished writing it. Check that all the following are correct, ticking the checklist as you go:

- ☐ spelling
- ☐ accents
- ☐ gender
- ☐ agreement of adjectives
- ☐ position of adjectives
- ☐ verb endings

2 Marks are awarded for "Accuracy". This means it is important to check your work and not throw away marks.

For a good grade in the writing assessment, you need to make sure all verbs are in the correct tense and that adjectives are correctly spelled and in the right position (see *Grammaire active*, pages 40–41 in your Students' Book).

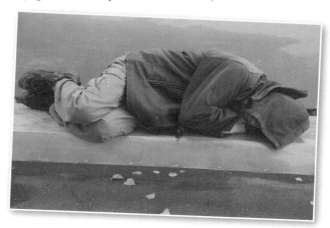

Grammaire active

Students' Book pages 40–41

adjectives ■ negatives

1 In this list of adjectives, underline the masculine ones and leave the feminine ones as they are. Then circle all the plural forms.

jolis	créatif	indépendant	généreuse	active
déterminée	grosses	heureux	travailleur	nouvelle
américain	italienne	anglaises	gallois	sportive	beaux

2 In each sentence, cross out the adjective that is in the wrong form.

a   J'ai un **nouveau / nouvelle** copain qui s'appelle Gianni.

b   Ses parents sont **italien / italiens**. Ils viennent de Rome.

c   Ils m'ont fait un cadeau pour Noël. Ils sont très **généreux / généreuse**!

d   Gianni est **sportifs / sportif**: il joue au tennis et au football et il fait du ski.

e   Je m'entends bien avec Gianni. Il est très **drôle / drôles**.

3 Write the correct letter in each box to match these French and English sentences.

a   Elles n'ont rien pour toi.

b   Je n'arrive jamais en retard.

c   Elle ne m'achète jamais de cadeau.

d   N'invitez personne!

e   Ils ne regardent jamais la télé.

1   Don't invite anyone. ☐

2   They have nothing for you. ☐

3   I never arrive late. ☐

4   They never watch TV. ☐

5   She never buys me a present. ☐

4 Use the words in brackets to make the sentences negative.

a   Je vais au cinéma (ne ... jamais)

_____

b   Buvez! (ne ... rien)

_____

c   Max est marié. (ne ... plus)

_____

5 Translate the negative sentences in activity 4 into English.

a   _____

b   _____

c   _____

Checklist

Fill in the checklist according to how confident you feel.

Key

☺	I know/can do this very well
☺	I'm not too sure I know/can do this
☹	I don't know/cannot do this well enough

Unit 1B Vivre ensemble	How confident am I?
I can **1** describe my personality and other people's	
2 describe relationships with family members and others (who I get on with)	
3 discuss recent changes in family life	
4 talk about my future plans regarding relationships and marriage	
5 talk about a social issue (young people in prison)	
6 discuss the issue of poverty	
Skills **7** use a variety of ways to learn vocabulary	
8 pronounce adjective endings correctly	
9 ask for clarification	
10 pronounce vowel sounds accurately	
11 recognise and use words that express opposing ideas	
12 scan a text for specific details	
13 recognise and use key words for giving an opinion	
Grammar **14** agree adjectives and use them in the correct position	
15 use possessive adjectives (*mon, ma, mes,* etc.)	
16 use subject pronouns (*je, tu, il,* etc.)	
17 use *si* + verb in present tense	
18 recognise and use different negatives	
19 make comparisons (*plus … que, moins … que*)	

Unit 2A Passe-temps et médias

Controlled Assessment: Speaking

Students' Book pages 60–61

Your teacher is going to interview you about computers and the Internet.

Preparing the task

1 You will have time to prepare the task using your Students' Book. Make sure you read over pages 60–61 and have all the basic language you will need.

2 There are opportunities to show off your knowledge of tenses. Decide how you will talk about whether you will use the computer this evening.

Example: *Je vais utiliser l'ordinateur pour aller sur Facebook, J'écrirai des emails, J'ai l'intention de faire des recherches sur Internet, etc.*

Use the imperfect to say how people used to communicate.

Example: *Comme il n'y avait pas d'emails, on écrivait des lettres.*

3 Remember to extend your answers where possible. Try to give reasons for what you say.

Example: *J'utilise mon ordinateur pour aller sur Facebook, parce que c'est très pratique si je veux rester en contact avec mes copines.*

4 Think of synonyms so that you are not always repeating the same words.

Example: *C'est un danger/un risque/un inconvénient/un désavantage.*

Performing the task

1 Listen carefully to your teacher's questions and be prepared to help the conversation to develop naturally. Eye contact, facial expressions and hand gestures will help your pace and expression come across well.

To keep going, follow this pattern: Fact /opinion > reason > example in the past or future.

2 Marks are awarded for "Pronunciation and Intonation".

You'll get extra marks for **consistently good accent and intonation**, so check in advance with your teacher if there are any words you are not sure how to pronounce. (The pronunciation guide on pages 9 and 10 is worth revising too.)

Controlled Assessment: Writing

✎ Students' Book pages 62–63

Write a letter or email to a French penfriend explaining what you do in your free time.

Preparing the task

1 Think of the vocabulary and grammar you will need, as well as specific phrases for writing an informal letter.

You can start with *Cher* + name for a boy or *Chère* + name for a girl.

Appropriate ending: *Amicalement* or *Ton copain* (for a boy) or *Ta corespondante* (for a girl) + your own name.

2 Try to incorporate the writing strategies you have learnt while working on this unit:

page 49   Different ways of giving reasons

page 55   Using a dictionary to check verb forms

page 51   Using synonyms to add variety

Look back over previous units too to remind yourself of other strategies to improve what you write.

3 Write in full sentences and try to link ideas so that the overall description reads well. Use unusual linking words (*surtout, sauf, par contre, en revanche, pourtant*) – see page 57 in your Students' Book, as well as the more common ones (*et, ou, mais*).

Writing the task

1 This is when you realise how valuable all your planning is! Keep to language you know well. You are allowed to use a dictionary to check words (not just spellings, but gender too) and don't forget the verb tables. But use it sparingly. If you look up every other word, you will not finish in time.

2 Marks are awarded for "Range of Language". As well as providing all the information you are asked for in accurate French, have you:

☐ used a variety of verbs to describe your activities (e.g. *jouer, faire, écouter* …)?

☐ used verb + infinitive correctly (e.g. *j'aime aller à la piscine, je voudrais faire du ski,* …)?

☐ added detail (e.g. *tous les jours, le lundi soir, parce que j'adore les jeux,* …)?

☐ included some extended sentences using linking words?

☐ shown that you know how to talk about past, present and future?

Grammaire active

Students' Book pages 58–59

> **imperfect tense ■ direct and indirect object pronouns**

1 Cross out all the verbs in this list that are not in the imperfect.

pouvais	peuvent
aimais	aimé
avons	avait
allait	allons
sont allés	allaient
étais	es
été	était
jouons	jouais

2 Use the remaining imperfect tense verbs to fill in the gaps in this text.

Quand j' ___*étais*___ petit, j'aimais beaucoup le sport. Mon sport préféré,

c' _____ le basket. Je _____ dans une équipe et on _____

des matchs tous les dimanches. On _____ à l'entraînement deux fois par

semaine. Les joueurs _____ aussi à la piscine deux fois par mois, mais moi,

je ne _____ pas parce que j' _____ allergique à l'eau de piscine.

3 Circle the correct pronouns: *le, la, l'* or *les.*

Example: Tu aimes mon T-shirt? Oui, je **le** /**l'** aime beaucoup.

a Tu regardes les infos tous les soirs? Oui, je **les** / **la** regarde tous les soirs.

b Tu as lu ce magazine? Oui, je **les** / **l'** ai lu.

c Il préfère la musique classique? Oui, il **le** / **la** préfère.

d Tu veux voir le film romantique? Oui, je veux **le** / **l'** voir.

e Tes copains aiment bien ce jeu vidéo? Oui, ils **l'** / **les** aiment bien.

4 Fill in the gaps in these sentences with *lui* or *leur.*

a Mes copains? Je _____ téléphone régulièrement.

b Voici Karine. Tu dois _____ donner son DVD.

c Tu n'as pas parlé à Marc? Envoie- _____ un SMS.

d Mes parents? Je vais _____ parler demain.

Checklist

Fill in the checklist according to how confident you feel.

Key

☺	I know/can do this very well
😐	I'm not too sure I know/can do this
☹	I don't know/cannot do this well enough

Unit 2A Passe-temps et médias	How confident am I?
I can **1** talk about my leisure activities	
2 discuss the advantages and disadvantages of different leisure activities	
3 say what type of music I like and why	
4 describe clothes and my view of fashion	
5 talk about shopping and money	
6 compare past and present technology	
7 discuss the pros and cons of social networking sites	
Skills **8** use a variety of structures to give reasons	
9 use synonyms	
10 use a dictionary to check verb tenses	
11 convert common word endings from French to English	
12 use related words to help work out the meaning of unfamiliar words	
13 spot link words that change meaning	
Grammar **14** use the comparative and superlative of adverbs	
15 recognise possessive pronouns (*le mien, le tien*, etc.)	
16 use direct and indirect object pronouns	
17 recognise and use imperfect tense verbs	
18 use modal verbs (*je peux, je veux, je dois*, etc.)	

Unit 2B Voyages et vacances

Controlled Assessment: Speaking

Students' Book pages 78–79

You are going to have a conversation with your teacher about holidays.

Preparing the task

1 Read the questions on page **78** of the Students' Book and think of how you will answer each one. You will need to:

> **Talk about summer activities**
> *aller à la piscine*
> *jouer au foot*, etc.

> **Describe your ideal holiday**
> *un pays chaud*
> *au bord de la mer*, etc.

> **Describe a past holiday**
> *Je suis parti(e) … / Je suis allé(e) …*
> *Nous avons visité … / On a fait …*, etc.

> **Talk about a future holiday**
> *Je vais aller … / J'irai …*
> *On va partir … / On visitera …*, etc.

2 Make notes to help you remember all the things you want to say. Remember you are only allowed 5 bullet points of a maximum of 8 words each. One of your bullet points could be a checklist of what you need to include to get a higher mark.

Example:

☐ opinions   ☐ future

☐ reasons   ☐ linking words

☐ past   ☐ *si* + imperfect

3 To show off how well you know verbs, try to vary from the *je* form now and again by using *on* or *nous* where others are involved.

Example: *Je suis allé(e) en Espagne avec ma mère. On a pris l'avion …*
Nous avons visité …

Performing the task

1 When answering questions, remember to use the language you prepared so you know what you say is accurate. You will feel more confident that way. If you do slip up, don't panic. You do not have to be 100% perfect to get a good mark.

2 Marks are awarded for "Range and Accuracy of language", which means you need to use a range of vocabulary including some complex structures.

To get top marks use justifying words like *parce que, car* or *ça me permet de*. And don't forget to include verbs to talk about the past and the future as well as the present.

Controlled Assessment: Writing

Students' Book pages 80–81

Write an account of a recent holiday or day trip you have been on for a travel blog.

Preparing the task

1 Prepare the task using the list on page 80 of your Students' Book. You could make a mind map.

Example:

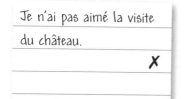

Torquay
avec mes parents
sud-ouest de l'Angleterre
2 semaines
en août

2 Pay particular attention to useful verbs. Most of what you write will be in the perfect tense. Remember that verbs of movement often form their perfect tense with *être* instead of *avoir*, e.g. *J'ai regardé* but *Je suis allé(e)*. Use the imperfect for descriptions or to say what you thought, e.g. *Il y avait beaucoup de choses à faire alors c'était très intéressant*.

3 Think about the purpose of the text you are writing. Here it is a travel blog. Make sure your text is interesting to read: it must be relevant and detailed.

Writing the task

1 Always remember to do a rough draft first. Read it with a critical eye and think of ways it could be improved. Be sure to check your work following the advice on page 8 of this book.

2 Marks are awarded for "Content". For a good grade in the writing assessment, you need to include plenty of relevant information and express yourself clearly. Don't just give facts. Explain your ideas and points of view too.

Example:

Je n'ai pas aimé la visite du château. ✗	Je n'ai pas vraiment aimé la visite du château parce que le guide parlait trop vite et je n'ai rien compris. ✓

Grammaire active

Students' Book pages 76–77

imperative ■ talking about the future

1 Rewrite these sentences using an imperative, to make an instruction saying what someone must do.
Example: Tu dois visiter ce musée, il est super! > Visite ce musée!

a Tu peux tourner à gauche et ensuite prendre la première à droite.

_____

b Anya, Léo, il faut prendre le bus!

_____

c Tu dois venir avec moi!

_____

d Tu peux réserver une chambre à l'hôtel, s'il te plaît?

_____

e Il faut faire attention sur la route, les enfants.

_____

2 Translate these sentences about the future into English.

a Je vais aller en France l'année prochaine.

_____

b Tu vas partir en vacances en juillet?

_____

c Il va aller au bord de la mer.

_____

d Elle va faire du camping.

_____

e Les profs vont être plus sévères cette année.

_____

3 Translate these sentences into French, using *aller* + infinitive.

a I am going to speak French every day.

_____

b Are you going to go camping?

_____

c The excursions are going to be very interesting.

_____

d We are going to visit Paris.

_____

e My grandmother is going to come by car.

_____

Checklist

Fill in the checklist according to how confident you feel.

Key

☺	I know/can do this very well
☺	I'm not too sure I know/can do this
☹	I don't know/cannot do this well enough

Unit 2B Voyages et vacances	How confident am I?
I can **1** discuss where to go on holiday	
2 ask the way and give directions	
3 ask someone out	
4 accept or refuse an invitation	
5 ask for/give information about tourist attractions	
6 describe a holiday or a day trip	
Skills	
7 use intonation to identify a question or a statement in spoken French	
8 predict vocabulary I might hear before a listening activity	
9 skim a text for gist	
10 use strategies to work out the meaning of unfamiliar words	
11 identify verb tenses when I listen	
12 use a variety of tenses when I speak or write	
Grammar **13** use a range of question words and forms	
14 use the imperative to give instructions	
15 recognise the future tense	
16 use the preposition *à*	
17 use modal verbs, including the conditional to be polite	
18 use *si* + imperfect tense to make a suggestion	
19 use verb + *à* or *de* + infinitive	
20 use *si* + imperfect + conditional	

Unit 3A Chez moi et aux alentours

Controlled Assessment: Speaking

Students' Book pages 96–97

You are going to have a conversation with your teacher about a special occasion you recently celebrated with your family.

Preparing the task

1 Choose a special occasion to talk about. It may not be one you have actually celebrated recently but make sure it is one that you know enough about to be able to describe and narrate in detail.

2 Look back at pages 84–85 of your Students' Book. Note down any words/expressions and tenses you find there which will be useful for your own conversation. Make lists.

opening phrases
Une fête inoubliable pour moi, c'était quand ...
Moi, la fête que je n'oublierai jamais, c'est ...

verbs to say what took place (perfect)
J'ai eu ... J'ai adoré ... on a dansé ...
On est tous allés ... on a fait la fête...

to describe and say what it was like (imperfect)
c'était super ... il y avait du monde ...

verbs to say what had happened before the party (pluperfect)
ils étaient allés ... ils avaient acheté ...

interesting words
fête de famille; plats traditionnels; des ballons et des banderoles

linking words
et ... alors ... donc ...
quand ... ... que ...

3 Condense your ideas down to 40 words and/or prepare visual clues (drawings, photos, etc.). You may want to note a couple of linking words to remind you to make longer sentences.
Example: *une fête que...* ❤ → *une fête que j'aime beaucoup.*

Performing the task

1 When answering the questions, remember to use the vocabulary and linking words you feel most confortable with to extend your sentences and expand your ideas. This is no time to try something new!

2 You'll be assessed on "Range and accuracy of language", which means how varied your vocabulary is and how correct your sentences are.
For a good grade in the speaking assessment, try using a **range of vocabulary** and some **complex structures**. For example, say "*C'était fantastique!*" rather than "*Super*". Become confident at making longer sentences, for instance using *qui* and *que*. Practise well and be ambitious!

Controlled Assessment: Writing

Students' Book pages 98–99

A French teenager from your twin town will be staying with you for a week. You have been asked to write to him telling him about your town in French so that he will feel at home when he arrives.

Preparing the task

1 Prepare the task using your Students' Book. Use Unit 3A to make sure you have the necessary language to speak about your home and local area:

pages 86–87 = about your home

pages 88–89 = about the sort of region you live in

pages 90–91 = about your town, its features and facilities

pages 92–93 = about family and family life

2 In this task, you are expected to use descriptive language. Revise the grammar you will need in order to do that well.

Refer to *Grammaire active*, pages 94–95 in your Students' Book.

Practise using relative pronouns to make your descriptions richer and fuller and to extend your sentences.

Writing *J'habite dans une ville pittoresque. Ma ville attire beaucoup de touristes* is good.

Writing *J'habite dans une ville pittoresque qui attire beaucoup de touristes* is better! Think of how you could complete these sentences about your own home and local area:

J'habite dans une maison/un appartement qui (est) ... (moderne/confortable) ...

C'est dans un quartier que (je trouve) ... (agréable/moche/ennuyeux) ...

Ma ville est dans une région où (il y a/on trouve) ... (des sites intéressants) ...

3 Remember to show off your knowledge of tenses, even when you think the topic doesn't lend itself to it. Here, for example, you could refer to:
- how long you've lived where you are now (present tense and *depuis*)
- where you used to live before (imperfect)
- what has recently happened in town (perfect)
- what will take place when your visitor is there (future), etc.

4 Remember the purpose of the text you are writing. Here, it is a letter to a French person of your own age. Revise the French you will need to write the opening and the closing phrases of an informal letter, e.g. *Cher/Chère ...*

Writing the task

1 Always remember to use the appropriate form of address in the letter. Here, it will be *tu* as you're addressing someone your own age although you might not know him/her.

2 You'll be assessed on "Range of language" which means how varied your choice of vocabulary is and how sophisticated you can make your sentences.

For a good grade in the writing assessment, make sure you write some **longer and more complex sentences** using linking words and relative pronouns. Think *"QQO"* (*qui, que, où*): it will push your grade up!

Grammaire active

Students' Book pages 94–95

y ■ ce/cet/cette/ces ■ qui/que/où

1 Transform the second sentence using *y* to avoid repetition.

Example: J'habite à Belleville depuis un an = J'y habite depuis un an.

a J'ai une grande chambre. Je mets tous mes livres dans ma chambre.

_____

b Je n'aime pas le sud de la France. Je ne vais jamais dans le sud de la France.

_____

c C'est un endroit très calme. Les touristes adorent aller dans cet endroit.

_____

2 Fill the gaps in these sentences with *ce, cette, cet* or *ces*.

a _____ appartement est très agréable, tu ne trouves pas?

b Il y a trop de choses dans _____ pièce.

c _____ jardins sont vraiment magnifiques, surtout au printemps!

d _____ île attire beaucoup les touristes qui aiment la plage.

e Comment s'appelle _____ pays francophone situé à côté de l'Algérie?

3 Rearrange these groups of words to make sentences with *qui, que* and *où*.

a C'est une j'adore région que

_____

b J'aime beaucoup visiter les de musées villes qui ont

_____

c Il y avait qui des magasins ont fermé l'an dernier

_____

d un quartier beaucoup à faire Je cherche il y a pour les jeunes où

_____

4 On a separate sheet, translate the sentences in activity 3 into English.

Checklist

Fill in the checklist according to how confident you feel.

Key

☺	I know/can do this very well
😐	I'm not too sure I know/can do this
☹	I don't know/cannot do this well enough

Unit 3A Chez moi et aux alentours	How confident am I?
I can **1** say how I celebrated a special occasion at home	
2 describe my home	
3 describe my region, where it is and what it is like	
4 describe my town	
5 discuss the features and facilities of my town	
6 describe a French-speaking area	
Skills **7** use linking words for a narration (*puis, après*, etc.)	
8 improve my pronunciation by reading aloud	
9 anticipate the vocabulary needed for a topic	
10 use stragegies to work out the meaning of unfamiliar words	
11 use adverbs of intensity (*très, beaucoup, tellement*)	
12 use strategies to make sure I understand people's opinions when listening	
13 use relative pronouns to add information and extend sentences	
Grammar **14** recognise the pluperfect tense	
15 use emphatic pronouns (*moi, toi, ...*)	
16 use demonstrative adjectives (*ce, cette, cet, ces*)	
17 use *depuis* with a present tense	
18 use relative pronouns (*qui, que, où*)	
19 recognise the relative pronoun *dont*	
20 use the pronoun *y*	

Unit 3B Notre monde

Controlled Assessment: Speaking

🔖 Students' Book pages 114–115

You are going to be interviewed by your teacher. You are a contestant in this year's Mr/Ms Green World competition. You have to show how environmentally-friendly you are.

Preparing the task

1 Prepare by making some notes on a mind map. Use key words only!

- holidays
- at home
- shopping
- **Mr/Ms Green World**
- food and drink
- transport
- hobbies

2 Prepare examples for each of the six areas on the mind map.
Example: *Je vais au collège à pied tous les jours, même quand il pleut.*

_____

_____

_____

_____

_____

_____

3 Now condense your notes down to 5 bullet points, each a maximum of 8 words, as you would have to for the controlled assessment.

Performing the task

1 Try to find a way to use more than one tense, e.g. by giving examples of what you have done (past tense) and what you do regularly (present tense). Rehearse your talk. Sound as enthusiastic as you can – you want to win!

2 Marks are awarded for "Communication". This means you need to include plenty of information and points of view and you must put them across clearly. You can develop them by adding detail (Where? When? Why? How?) and giving examples.

Controlled Assessment: Writing

Students' Book pages 116–117

You are going to write a publicity leaflet advertising an ecotourism holiday in a French-speaking country.

Preparing the task

1 Start by reading up as much as possible about your chosen destination. Do some research on the Internet using a French search engine, e.g. www.google.fr.

2 You are going to write around **300** words. If you use the headings below, that means about **60** words for each.

3 Make notes (key words only!) about each of these headings.
* location and surroundings

* accommodation

* meals

* activities

* advantages of this kind of holiday

Writing the task

1 Be sure you're making the most of your French. Check that you have used:
- [ ] plenty of positive adjectives and opinions
- [ ] more than one tense if possible
- [ ] two or three different linking words

2 Marks are awarded for "Content" so make sure you do your research and have something interesting and relevant to say. As you are writing a publicity leaflet, make sure you have been positive and convincing. Explain your ideas clearly, using language that you know.

Grammaire active

Students' Book pages 112–113

conjunctions

1 Draw lines to link each of these English conjunctions with its French equivalent.

and	mais
but	et
or	donc
so	ou
without	sans

2 Write in the missing conjunctions to complete these speech bubbles.

a Je prends une douche, pas un bain _____ je recycle les papiers.

b Tu manges de la viande _____ tu es végétarien?

c Il y a un centre de recyclage en face de mon appartement, _____ je recycle tout.

d Il y a de l'eau _____ on ne peut pas la boire parce qu'elle n'est pas potable.

e On doit apprendre à vivre _____ polluer la planète.

3 Translate the sentences in the speech bubbles into English.

a _____

b _____

c _____

d _____

e _____

Checklist

Fill in the checklist according to how confident you feel.

Key

☺	I know/can do this very well
☺	I'm not too sure I know/can do this
☹	I don't know/cannot do this well enough

Unit 3B Notre monde	How confident am I?
I can	
1 describe environmental problems	
2 talk about my hopes for the future of our planet	
3 discuss transport	
4 say how I am environmentally friendly	
5 explain what ecotourism is about	
Skills	
6 read a text for gist and for detail	
7 decode unfamiliar vocabulary	
8 avoid word–for–word translations	
9 cope with 'false friends'	
10 get the most out of listening more than once	
11 get maximum marks for each question	
Grammar	
12 use adverbs of time	
13 use the comparative and superlative	
14 use conjunctions	
15 recognise the subjunctive	

Unit 4A La vie à l'école

Controlled Assessment: Speaking

Students' Book pages 132–133

You are going to have a conversation with your teacher about the pros and cons of having a part-time job while at school.

Preparing the task

1 Use your Students' Book to make lists of ideas and phrases for each of the questions. Then practise answering the questions, picking items from your lists as you would from an "à la carte" menu! Mix and match and do this several times to increase variety and fluency.

Example:

> **Q**: What are the best ways of making money when you are still at school?

A: phrases

On peut ...
C'est aussi possible de/d' ...
C'est bien de ...

ideas

travailler dans un supermarché
laver des voitures
faire les courses pour des personnes âgées

2 These questions offer you a chance to show off your knowledge of tenses. Think of creative ways of using tenses in your reply. For example, illustrate what you say with examples from the past or projects for the future.

Look at *Grammaire active*, pages 130–131 in your Students' Book and revise all the tenses you know.

Example:

> **Q**: What are the benefits of having a part-time job, apart from money?

A: present: *on apprend des choses*

imperfect + perfect: *Par exemple, quand je travaillais au supermarché, j'ai appris ...*

future: *Avec de l'expérience, on trouvera un emploi plus facilement.*

Performing the task

1 Try to respond to questions as naturally as possible: keep eye contact with the teacher, use your hands while you speak, use facial expressions: it will all help you sound more authentic and natural.

2 You'll be assessed on "Interaction and fluency", which means how well you answer the questions in terms of your ideas and of how comfortable you are with the language.

For a good grade in the speaking assessment, you're expected to extend your answers **beyond the minimum**, for instance by providing examples which will make what you say more interesting. So no more "yes/no" answers!

Controlled Assessment: Writing

Students' Book pages 134–135

You are writing an article for the next issue of the school newsletter about what you think works and what doesn't work in your school and what improvements you would suggest.

Preparing the task

1 To be effective, your article needs to be structured carefully. Start planning your arguments using a mind map.

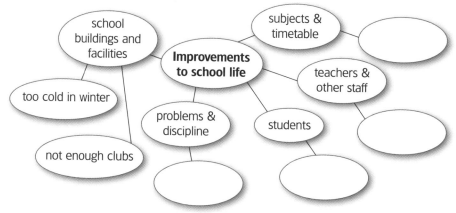

2 Use Unit 4A of your Students' Book to make sure you have the necessary language for talking about school life:

pages 120–121 = about subjects and timetable

pages 122–123 = about school life

pages 128–129 = about problems and pressures

3 For vocabulary you don't already know, use a dictionary (some good dictionaries are also available online) and note down the new words. However, as far as possible, use vocabulary that you do already know.

4 You need to write 250–300 words. Work out how many words you can use for each section so that you don't run out of words after a couple of paragraphs! Remember, you will need to allow for a short introduction and a conclusion.

Writing the task

1 Remember the writing techniques you have learnt in English, e.g. using persuasive language to convince an audience, and apply them here. What about using a few rhetorical questions too? e.g. *How would you like to work in a freezing classroom?*

2 You'll be assessed on "Accuracy" which means how correct your grammar and spelling are.

For a good grade in the writing assessment, the examiner will expect that your **verb and tense formations are usually correct** which means you know which tense to use and what verb ending is needed. Well worth leaving a few minutes at the end of the assessment to read through your text and check those verb agreements!

Grammaire active

Students' Book pages 130–131

revision of tenses

1 Circle all the verbs that are talking about the past and underline those that refer to the future.

je vais prendre	on a vu	tu aimeras	elle faisait	ils sont sortis
vous comprendrez	ous avons travaillé	je lisais		il va faire
tu vas voir	on ira		elles ont pris	vous étiez

2 Translate these sentences about the future into English.

a Je vais travailler dans un magasin l'année prochaine.

_____

b Tu vas faire un petit boulot?

_____

c Il va aller au lycée le samedi matin.

_____

d Elle va manger à la cantine aujourd'hui.

_____

e Les profs vont être plus sévères cette année.

_____

3 Perfect or imperfect? Cross out the verb that is wrong each time there is a choice.

a L'année dernière, Ali **a fait** / **faisait** un stage dans un office de tourisme. **C'était** / **Ça a été** intéressant.

b Quand j'allais au collège, **j'ai pris** / **je prenais** le bus tous les matins.

c Quand mon père **a été** / **était** jeune, il **a acheté** / **achetait** une moto.

d Marie et Léa **oubliaient** / **ont oublié** leurs devoirs ce matin.

e À l'école primaire, on **a écouté** / **écoutait** des histoires.

4a Translate the sentences from activity 3 into English.

a _____

b _____

c _____

d _____

e _____

4b Now look at your translations and, on a separate sheet, translate them back into French. Check against the original sentences in activity 3.

Checklist

Fill in the checklist according to how confident you feel.

Key

☺	I know/can do this very well
😐	I'm not too sure I know/can do this
☹	I don't know/cannot do this well enough

Unit 4A La vie à l'école	How confident am I?
I can	
1 talk about the subjects I study at school	
2 describe my school and school life	
3 describe my ideal school	
4 compare school life in different countries	
5 say if I have a part-time job	
6 talk about advantages/disadvantages of part-time jobs	
7 talk about problems and pressure in school	
Skills	
8 use prediction to help when listening	
9 use phrases to compare and contrast	
10 cope with false friends	
11 give detailed answers	
12 use a variety of structures e.g. to express an opinion	
Grammar	
13 use *depuis* with the imperfect tense	
14 recognise the passive voice in the present tense	
15 recognise a perfect infinitive	
16 recognise reflexive verbs in the perfect tense	
17 understand which tenses to use when	

Unit 4B Gagner sa vie

Controlled Assessment: Speaking

Students' Book pages 150–151

You are going to be interviewed for a job by your teacher. You will play the role of the candidate and your teacher will be the interviewer.

Preparing the task

1 Prepare for the task by making sure you have the basic language needed to talk about yourself in a job interview situation. Also, think about ways of expanding and making spontaneous comments as you go. This will get you extra marks.

Example: qualifications – if you have none yet, think of what you **hope** to achieve in the future

2 Make sure you include opportunities to show off your use of tenses. For instance, even if you are not asked what job you'd like to do later on, try and mention it.

Example: *Je voudrais ce job parce que ce serait une bonne expérience pour moi, comme je voudrais travailler dans le tourisme plus tard.*

3 Use the Students' Book and make a thorough audit of all the speaking strategies you have covered. Think of others you may have used and found useful.

Example:

1A	page 13	Making liaisons
	page 15	Using tone to sound convincing
	page 19	Giving examples
1B	page 33	Pronouncing vowel sounds correctly, etc.

4 Listen to lots of French (on the CDs that go with this Workbook and the Students' Book, on French radio or TV channels, or on French DVDs) to get a feel for the "melody" of the language. This will help you to understand it.

Record yourself speaking. Get your teacher and/or the French assistant to listen and ask for help and advice. Re-record yourself a week later and compare. Have you improved?

Performing the task

1 In a role-play like this, you will need to think of "performing" your role. Think yourself into character: use facial expressions, hand gestures and be expressive in your intonation in order to convince the interviewer (and examiner) that you're the best person for the job!

2 You'll be assessed on "Pronunciation and Intonation" which means how well you pronounce individual words as well as whole sentences.

You'll get extra marks if you have a **good accent** and **accurate intonation**.

So speak slowly and clearly, take your time and, most importantly, don't panic!

Controlled Assessment: Writing

Students' Book pages 152–153

You are writing a covering letter for an online agency that you are using to find a summer placement in a French-speaking country.

Preparing the task

1 Think of the vocabulary and grammar you will need in order to write the letter, as well as specific phrases and conventions for writing a formal letter.

Example: Starting with *Madame, ...* and ending with something like *Je vous prie d'agréer, Madame, l'expression de mes meilleurs sentiments.*

2 Use the Students' Book and make a thorough audit of all the writing strategies you have covered. Think of others you may have used and found useful.

Example:

1A	page 13	Using determiners correctly
	page 17	Using adverbs
	page 21	Writing longer sentences
2A	page 49	Giving reasons for opinions
	page 55	Dictionary skills
4B	page 140	Letter writing

3 The more you read, the more fluent your writing is likely to be. Re-read example letters and other texts in your Students' Book to remind you of different ways of phrasing certain things and extending sentences.

Make a note of more unusual expressions that you think you can reuse in the assessment comfortably and that are likely to earn you bonus marks!

Writing the task

1 Imagine yourself as the person reading your letter. Would you find it interesting? Would your interest be maintained right through to the end? Would you want to give that person a job? If the answer is 'no', think again about how you can make your writing more exciting!

2 During the writing assessment, keep an eye on the clock and leave yourself some time for checking your work at the end. To meet the assessment criteria, your priorities are:

Content
- ☐ Include all the information you are asked for.
- ☐ Write clearly defined paragraphs.
- ☐ Include opinions.

Range of Language
- ☐ Write extended sentences using linking words.
- ☐ Use a variety of tenses and structures.

Accuracy
- ☐ Use tense and verb endings correctly.
- ☐ Use adjective endings correctly.

Bonne chance!

Grammaire active

🔊 Students' Book pages 148–149

> conditional ■ verbs + *à/de* + infinitive ■ *en* + present participle

1 Fill the gaps in these sentences with the verb *vouloir* in the correct form of the conditional.

a Plus tard, elle _____ faire ses études à l'étranger.

b Je _____ réussir mon GCSE et continuer mes études.

c Ils _____ faire leur stage dans un hôtel.

d Est-ce que tu _____ travailler pendant les vacances?

e Mon ami et moi, nous _____ prendre une année sabbatique.

f Vous _____ travailler ou voyager?

2 Fill the gaps in these sentences with the correct preposition *à* or *de/d'*. Leave blank if no preposition is needed.

a Je vais apprendre _____ conduire.

b Mes parents m'ont beaucoup aidé _____ trouver un job.

c Je préfère _____ prendre une année sabbatique avant d'aller à l'université.

d Elle ne peut pas _____ aller à l'entretien.

e Ils ont décidé _____ arrêter leurs études.

f Tu as essayé _____ trouver un job dans un supermarché?

g Vous commencez _____ travailler la semaine prochaine.

h Je veux absolument _____ continuer mes études de français!

3 On a separate sheet, translate the sentences from activity 2 into English.

4 Complete these sentences by using *en* + present participles of the verbs in brackets.

Example: Je vais apprendre le français (écouter) en *écoutant* le CD-Rom.

a Tu réussiras (travailler) en _____ dur.

b Elle se relaxe (sortir) en _____ avec ses amies.

c C'est plus rapide (aller) en _____ à pied.

d Il s'est amélioré (prendre) en _____ des cours du soir.

5 Translate these sentences into French using *en* + a present participle.

a You'll understand better if you listen to the French radio often.

   Tu comprendras mieux en _____

b You'll speak more easily if you speak with the French assistant.

   _____

c You can learn vocabulary by writing the words ten times.

   _____

d Don't watch TV while doing your homework.

   _____

Checklist

Fill in the checklist according to how confident you feel.

Key

☺	I know/can do this very well
☺	I'm not too sure I know/can do this
☹	I don't know/cannot do this well enough

Unit **4B Gagner sa vie**	How confident am I?
I can **1** understand job ads	
2 say which job would suit me best and why	
3 write my CV in French	
4 apply for a summer job	
5 do well in an interview	
6 describe my work experience	
7 discuss the advantages and disadvantages of different jobs	
Skills **8** use context for gist	
9 use accents and capital letters	
10 use word families to work out meaning	
11 be aware of formal/informal writing	
12 use formula phrases for letter writing	
13 reuse words from the question in my answer	
Grammar **14** recognise and use the conditional	
15 use expressions using the infinitive	
16 recognise *en* + present participle	

Answers

Listening practice (pages 11–14)

Exercise 1

1 cinema   **2** playing video games   **3** going out with friends
4 playing music in a band

Exercise 2

5 D   **6** E   **7** A   **8** C

Exercise 3

9 A/1   **10** C/3   **11** F/2

Exercise 4

12 A   **13** A   **14** B   **15** C   **16** C

Exercise 5

17 3   **18** gymnastics   **19** handball   **20** jogging

Exercise 6

21 studying is not motivating – more work experience
22 pollution – ecology lessons at school

Exercise 7

23 B   **24** A   **25** B   **26** B

Exercise 8

27 C   **28** E   **29** B   **30** D

Vocabulary in practice (pages 17–25)

Page 18

1 **a** timide   **b** têtu(e)   **c** drôle   **d** une douche   **e** un demi-frère
f l'ambiance   **g** heureux/heureuse   **h** travailleur/travailleuse
i un(e) adolescent(e)   **j** un vol

Page 19

7 un ouvre-bouteille – ouvre = *open*; bouteille = *bottle* > *bottle opener*
une poissonnerie – poisson = *fish* > *fish shop*
la politesse – poli = *polite* > *politeness*

Page 20

1 **Verbs**: j'ai, allez, descendre, avoir, tu vois, on est
3 je préfère > préférer   tu vas > aller   il a vu > voir   elle faisait > faire
on veut > vouloir   j'ai > avoir

4 Regular: aimer (*to like*), parler (*to speak*), finir (*to finish*), écouter (*to listen*), chanter (*to sing*)
Irregular: avoir (*to have*), faire (*to do/make*), voir (*to see*), être (*to be*), aller (*to go*)
5 Food and drink: manger, déjeuner, boire, goûter, cuisiner
Any topic: aider, faire, avoir, prendre, ajouter

Page 22

1 un – *a* (m)   une – *a* (f)   des – (*of*) the (pl)   le – *the* (m)
la – *the* (f)   les – *the* (pl)   de – *of* or *from*   de la – *of* or *from the* (f)
du – *of the* (m)   à – *at* or *to*   au – *to the* (m)   aux – *to the* (pl)
2 a I like the animals = I like animals.
b I sleep in the bedroom of my brother = I sleep in my brother's bedroom.
c I go to the high school the Saturday = I go to school on Saturdays.
d He is teacher of maths = He's a maths teacher.
e I have hurt at the leg = My leg hurts.
3 *after* – après   *and* – et   *because* – parce que   *before* – avant
but – mais   *first* – d'abord   *for instance* – par exemple   *then* – puis

Page 23

4 a Avant; Après   **b** parce qu'   **c** D'abord; puis
5 Past: hier (*yesterday*), la semaine dernière (*last week*), avant (*before*)
Present: maintenant (*now*), aujourd'hui (*today*), en ce moment (*at the moment*)
Future: demain (*tomorrow*), la semaine prochaine (*next week*), plus tard (*later on*)
6 a maintenant/aujourd'hui/en ce moment   **b** la semaine dernière/hier/avant
c la semaine prochaine/plus tard
7 *who?* – qui?   *when?* – quand?   *how much/many?* – combien?
where? – où?   *why?* – pourquoi?   *how?* – comment?   *which?* – quel(le)?
what? – qu'est-ce que ...?
8 a Où   **b** Quand   **c** Comment   **d** Combien   **e** Qu'est-ce que
f Qui

Page 24

1 Positive: j'aime, je préfère, ça m'intéresse
Negative: ça m'énerve, je déteste, ça ne me plaît pas
2 a intéressant, génial, sympa, passionnant
b ennuyeux, injuste, nul, inutile
4 *I'm going to* – je vais   *I want to* – je veux   *I would like to* – j'aimerais
I intend to – j'ai l'intention de   *I hope to* – j'espère

Page 25

6 *Un peu* – a bit   *assez* – quite   *très* – very   *vraiment* – really
trop – too
8 1 b   **2** a   **3** d   **4** c   **5** f   **6** e

Worksheets (pages 26–57)

1A Grammaire active (page 28)

1 a apprenez, faisons   **b** viennent, peuvent   **c** sors, dois
   d veut, part
2 a me, me, me   **b** se, se, se   **c** s', s'
3

	infinitive	present tense	perfect tense
-er	habiter	habitons	avons habité
-ir	finir	finit	a fini
-re	prendre	prennent	ont pris
irreg.	aller	vas	es allé

4 a des **b** de la **c** d' **d** de **e** de l', de la

1B Grammaire active (page 32)

1 masculine adjectives: jolis, créatif, indépendant, heureux, travailleur, américain, gallois, beaux
   plural forms: jolis, grosses, heureux, anglaises, gallois, beaux
2 a nouveau **b** italiens **c** généreux **d** sportif **e** drôle
3 1 d **2** a **3** b **4** e **5** c
4 a Je ne vais jamais au cinéma.
   b Ne buvez rien!
   c Max n'est plus marié.
5 a I never go to the cinema.
   b Don't drink anything!
   c Max isn't married any more.

2A Grammaire active (page 36)

1 Imperfect verbs are: pouvais, aimais, allait, étais, avait, allaient, était, jouais
2 étais (already filled in as example), était, jouais, avait, allait, allaient, pouvais, étais
3 a les **b** l' **c** la **d** le **e** l'
4 a leur **b** lui **c** lui **d** leur

2B Grammaire active (page 40)

1 a Tourne à gauche et prends la première à droite!
   b Anya, Léo, prenez le bus!
   c Viens avec moi!
   d Réserve une chambre à l'hôtel, s'il te plaît.
   e Faites attention sur la route, les enfants!
2 a I am going to go to France next year.
   b Are you going to go on holiday in July?
   c He is going to go to the seaside.
   d She is going to go camping.
   e The teachers are going to be stricter this year.

3 a Je vais parler français tous les jours.
b Tu vas/Vous allez faire du camping?
c Les excursions vont être très intéressantes.
d On va/Nous allons visiter Paris.
e Ma grand-mère va venir en voiture.

3A Grammaire active (page 44)
1 a J'y mets tous mes livres.   **b** Je n'y vais jamais.
c Les touristes adorent y aller.
2 a Cet **b** cette **c** Ces **d** Cette **e** ce
3 a C'est une région que j'adore.
b J'aime visiter les villes qui ont beaucoup de musées.
c Il y avait des magasins qui ont fermé l'an dernier.
d Je cherche un quartier où il y a beaucoup à faire pour les jeunes.
4 a It's a region (that) I love.
b I like visiting towns which have lots of museums.
c There used to be shops which closed last year.
d I'm looking for an area where there are lots of things for young people to do.

3B Grammaire active (page 48)
1 *and* – et; *but* – mais; *or* – ou; *so* – donc; *without* – sans
2 a et **b** ou **c** donc **d** mais **e** sans
3 a I have a shower, not a bath and I recycle paper.
b Do you eat meat or are you vegetarian?
c There is a recycling centre opposite my flat, so I recycle everything.
d There is water but you/we can't drink it because it is not drinking water.
e You/We must learn to live without polluting the planet.

4A Grammaire active (page 52)
1 Past: on a vu, elle faisait, ils sont sortis, nous avons travaillé, je lisais, elles ont pris, vous étiez
Future: je vais prendre, tu aimeras, vous comprendrez, il va faire, tu vas voir, on ira
2 a I am going to work in a shop next year.
b Are you going to do a part-time job?
c He is going to go to school on Saturday mornings.
d She is going to eat in the canteen today.
e The teachers are going to be stricter this year.
3 a a fait, C'était **b** je prenais **c** était, a acheté **d** ont oublié
e écoutait
4a a Last year, Ali did a work placement in a tourist office. It was interesting.
b When I went to school, I used to take the bus/go by bus every morning.
c When my father was young, he bought a motorbike.
d Marie and Léa forgot/have forgotten their homework this morning.
e At primary school, we used to listen to stories.

4B Grammaire active (page 56)

1 a voudrait **b** voudrais **c** voudraient **d** voudrais **e** voudrions
f voudriez
2 a à **b** à **c** – **d** – **e** d' **f** de **g** à **h** –
3 a I am going to learn to drive.
b My parents have helped me a lot to find a job.
c I prefer to have a year out before going to university.
d She can't go to the interview.
e They have decided to stop their studies.
f Have you tried to find a job in a supermarket?
g You start work next week.
h I definitely want to carry on studying French!
4 a Tu réussiras en travaillant dur.
b Elle se relaxe en sortant avec ses amies.
c C'est plus rapide en allant à pied.
d Il s'est amélioré en prenant des cours du soir.
5 a Tu comprendras mieux en écoutant souvent la radio.
b Tu parleras plus facilement en parlant avec l'assistant(e) français(e).
c Tu peux apprendre le vocabulaire en écrivant dix fois les mots.
d Ne regarde pas la télé en faisant tes devoirs.

CD track list

1 Copyright notice

Audio tracks for Foundation Workbook

2 p. 9, ex. 1
3 p. 9, ex. 2
4 p. 9, ex. 3
5 p. 9, ex. 4
6 p. 9, ex. 5
7 p. 10, ex. 6
8 p. 10, ex. 7
9 p. 10, ex. 8
10 p. 10, ex. 9
11 p. 10, Extra pronunciation practice
12 p. 11, ex. 1
13 p. 11, ex. 2
14 p. 12, ex. 3
15 p. 12, ex. 4
16 p. 13, ex. 5
17 p. 13, ex. 6
18 p. 14, ex. 7
19 p. 14, ex. 8

Audio tracks for Higher Workbook

20 p. 9, ex. 1
21 p. 9, ex. 2
22 p. 9, ex. 3
23 p. 9, ex. 4
24 p. 10, ex. 5
25 p. 10, ex. 6
26 p. 10, ex. 7
27 p. 10, ex. 8
28 p. 10, Extra pronunciation practice
29 p. 11, ex. 1
30 p. 11, ex. 2
31 p. 12, ex. 3
32 p. 13, ex. 4
33 p. 13, ex. 5
34 p. 14, ex. 6
35 p. 14, ex. 7